Dog Days

Musical *Tails* of My Rescue Dogs

Music by

Jennifer Eklund

PIANO PRONTO PUBLISHING

PianoPronto.com

Dog Days: Musical *Tails* of My Rescue Dogs

Jennifer Eklund

Copyright © 2013 by Jennifer Eklund. All Rights Reserved.

WARNING: The compositions, arrangements, text, and graphics in this publication are protected by copyright law. No part of this work may be duplicated or reprinted without the prior consent of the author.

ISBN 978-0-9899084-1-2

Printed in the United States of America

Piano Pronto Publishing, Inc.

PianoPronto.com

FOREWORD NOTES

The only thing I love more in life than music and the piano are my four-legged kids. I wanted to pay tribute to the joy they bring me on a daily basis by memorializing a day in their lives in music. I've adopted my dogs from two wonderful rescue organizations. As a thanks to the wonderful work these groups do day in and day out, a portion of the proceeds from the sale of these books will be donated to *Border Collies in Need* to help with the expenses incurred from fostering and placing homeless pets into their forever homes. It is my hope after you read their stories that you will be motivated to adopt instead of purchase your next pet. Here's a little explanation behind each piece to help bring you and your students closer to the music:

Morning Stretch ~ *This piece is a modern remix of Grieg's iconic "Morning Theme." There is nothing like the start of the day when the puppies first awaken and prepare for a busy day with a big stretch. Make sure to take your time in the last four measures of the piece—stretches are not meant to be rushed.*

Oh Snap! ~ *After you read Sydney's story you'll have good insight into her personality. She is my sassy, independent little diva, and her dirty blues theme music should be played with a heavy swing and lots of strong accents.*

On the Trail ~ *Megyn's theme music can be described in two words: mellow and lazy. This piece has a cowboy/western flair and is also played with a heavy swing, but without the heavy accenting of Sydney's piece. This piece should be played pretty slowly since Megyn is never in a hurry to do anything.*

End Game ~ *This piece is Megyn's "squirrel-stalking" piece. Most days the squirrels taunt her as they run back and forth on the telephone wire that sits above my back fence. Having the typical instincts of a border collie Megyn can exhibit laser-beam focus when stalking the squirrel, sometimes for hours on end. Her end game is always clear, but the squirrel is on to her, enjoys teasing her, and then scurries away into his tree.*

Tropical Breeze ~ *Being a dog is a tough job, so frequent siestas are a must! Both Sydney and Megyn enjoy laying in the breezeway in the backyard. It is their own little tropical paradise. This bossa nova inspired piece should help transport you as well—think of it as a musical vacation!*

The Chase ~ *The daily visit from the mailman marks the most chaotic time in our daily routine. As soon as Sydney hears the back of his truck open up upon his arrival, the madness breaks out. Sydney runs from her station on the back of the couch, flies through her dog door and races around the side of the house showing her distaste for his existence. Megyn joins in as well, but honestly I think she's just following the crowd. This fast and flashy showcase piece is sure to be a favorite with your students!*

New Kid on the Block ~ *It's tough being the new dog on the block, but Daisy approaches life with a carefree attitude that is captured perfectly in her jazzy theme song. Make sure to apply a heavy swing to all the eighth notes to enhance her bouncy puppy spirit.*

Walkin' Tall ~ *My girls have swag. When we go for walks their tails are always held high and they act as though they own the neighborhood. Their favorite walk in the summer months up by the local elementary school offers them a high ledge where they can "walk tall." This jazzy little swing number should exude confidence and fun!*

Lullaby ~ *Grieg often closed his sets of* Lyric Pieces *with simple understated melodies, and I wanted to do the same. Every day in our house closes with a simple belly rub at bedtime for all the girls, the perfect end to another day of puppy life.*

Morning Stretch

Edvard Grieg

Arr. Jennifer Eklund

Copyright © 2013 Piano Pronto Publishing, Inc.
All Rights Reserved | PianoPronto.com

Stretching

Sydney's *Tail*

a.k.a. "Little Monkey" & "The Sheriff"

My life started out kind of rough! My adoptive mommy doesn't know all the details except for what the rescue organization told her. Between you and me, I was on quite the adventure as a young puppy out running solo in the California desert. A lady truck-driver saw me running loose and was nice enough to stop and chase after me. I was pretty fast back then so I'm sure she got a workout! She put me in her 18-wheeler and off I went on a cross-country roadtrip, the most epic car-ride ever. After a stop in Mississippi we turned around and headed back to California where she handed me off to a friend of hers who worked for a rescue organization called *Diamonds in the Ruff.*

Back then I didn't even have a name; all my vet records just referred to me as "Girl." The rescue people made the ghastly error of renaming me "Chelsea" and I'm sure by the looks of my picture, and once you hear my theme music, you'll realize what a mistake that was!

It was June of 2005 when the other foster dogs and I were taken to the Pomona Pet Expo for an adoption event. That was the day I hit the jackpot! My mom adopted me that day even though when she was checking me over I was so distracted by all the other dogs around me I wouldn't even pay attention to her. I was about 10 months old then, tons of energy, and she had no idea what she was getting into! That was the day I got my forever home and I've had a pretty sweet life since then.

My mom renamed me "Sydney" after the main character from her favorite TV show *Alias.* Supposedly the character was a pretty tough and sassy little lady, so it was a perfect fit. Like most dogs I needed a job at my new home to keep me occupied between naps. I took it upon myself to take the job of guarding the front of the house. Luckily, my mom chose a house with a huge front window and a comfy couch. Most of the time you will find me lying on the back of the couch keeping an eye on things. I go a bit crazy everyday when the mailman shows up, and my mom thought it was worth writing a song about the whole thing ("The Chase").

I ran the whole show around here as the only child for the first few years. Then my mom adopted my sister Megyn and for the most part we are the best of friends, as long as Megyn does whatever I tell her to do. She's a pretty good deputy and companion. We like going for walks together, chasing the squirrels in the backyard, and occasionally wrestling in the living room. Some people say that I'm just like a cat and probably was one in my former life. I'm super independent and always doing my own thing, except at bedtime when I get my nightly belly-rub. Hey even the toughest cookies need a little affection sometimes. So here's my song "Oh Snap!" that mommy wrote to capture my personality—it's a pretty sassy little tune and I give it two paws up!

Oh Snap!

Jennifer Eklund

Moderate swing

simile

Copyright © 2013 Piano Pronto Publishing, Inc.
All Rights Reserved | PianoPronto.com

Straight (no swing)

Megyn's *Tail*

a.k.a. "Meggie Monster" & "The Deputy"

My life started out kind of rough as well and my adoptive mommy knows even less about my early life. What we do know is that I was left behind at my old house by the people who owned me when I was a puppy. They had lost their house to a foreclosure, packed up, moved away, but decided to leave me to fend for myself in the backyard. I was pretty terrified, hungry, and disappointed in my people. Animal Control found me eventually and took me to the shelter. I was so upset over losing my people that I wouldn't look at anybody in the shelter and was completely devastated and depressed. I was lying in my kennel with my back turned to the world because the world had turned its back on me.

I probably didn't have much time left to get adopted, but my prayers were answered when the people with *Border Collies in Need* came to save me from the shelter. I still didn't trust people, so I gave my foster moms a pretty hard time. I went to stay with my foster mom Kathy for a few weeks and she was awesome. She was the first person I opened up to after my ordeal. She would let me come up and snuggle with her on her bed, which was exactly what I needed.

In April of 2009 my future mommy saw a posting on the internet with my story. I guess she wasn't really looking to adopt another dog at the time, but my story really got under her skin and she decided to put in an adoption application. The rescuers were going to be pretty picky about who they sent me home with since I was still pretty emotionally fragile. The day mommy came to meet me at a pet adoption fair in San Pedro I was not in the mood to deal with people. While all my other foster friends sat eagerly in their kennel trying to attract the attention of their potential new parents, once again I was lying there with my back turned to everyone. When my adoptive mommy came to meet me I could tell she was going to love me forever and within an hour I was off to my forever home.

I had a rough time adjusting to home-life at first, but luckily my new little sister Sydney was welcoming and showed me the ropes. I was still scared to

meet new people for a couple years, but nowadays I love interacting with all humans. Sydney thought I needed a job so she assigned me to guard the back of the house. My personality is as mellow as can be so I'm definitely not your typical border collie. Luckily, other than the daily visit from my friend the squirrel, there's not much going on in the backyard, which leaves me plenty of time to loaf around and catch up on my napping. I'm the most gentle soul you'll ever meet and I would have never made it out of that shelter if it weren't for the folks at *Border Collies in Need*. Did I mention I love the piano too? Mommy has one of my dog beds right by the piano and everytime she starts playing my theme song "On the Trail" I sit there proudly listening to my melody. Life is sweet.

On the Trail

Jennifer Eklund

Copyright © 2013 Piano Pronto Publishing, Inc.
All Rights Reserved | PianoPronto.com

End Game

Jennifer Eklund

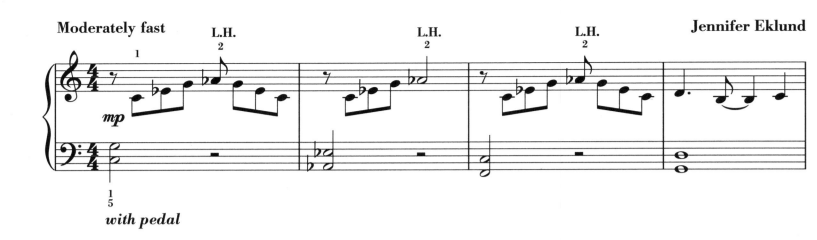

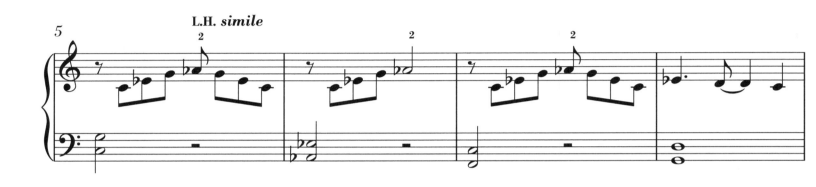

Copyright © 2013 Piano Pronto Publishing, Inc.
All Rights Reserved | PianoPronto.com

Tropical Breeze

Jennifer Eklund

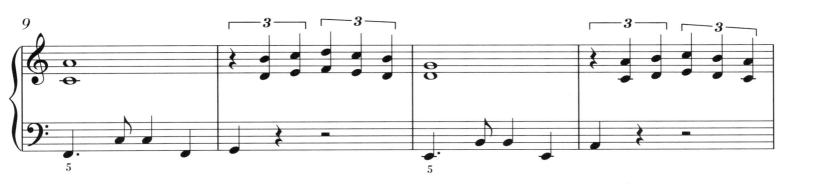

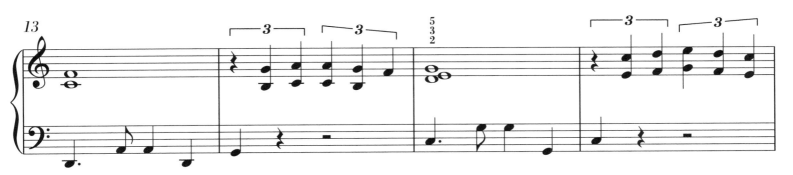

Copyright © 2013 Piano Pronto Publishing, Inc.
All Rights Reserved | PianoPronto.com

The Chase

Jennifer Eklund

Stems up: right hand
Stems down: left hand

Copyright © 2013 Piano Pronto Publishing, Inc.
All Rights Reserved | PianoPronto.com

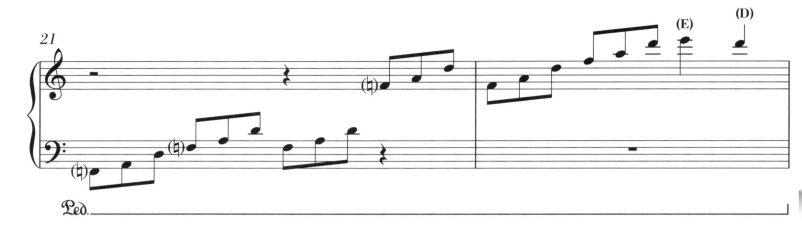

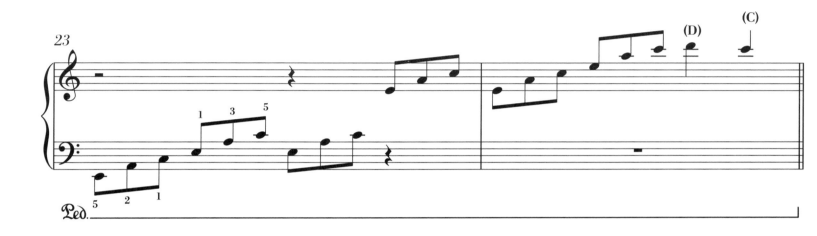

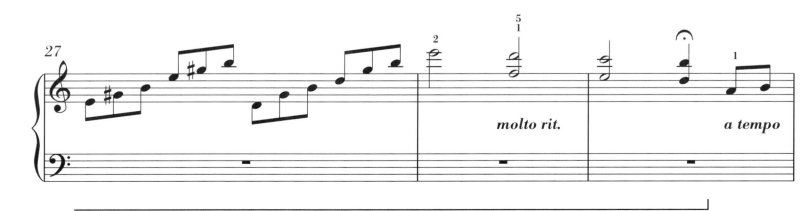

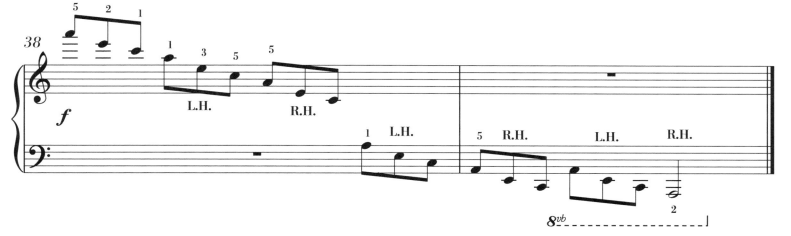

Daisy's *Tail*

a.k.a. "Daisy Boots"

Have you figured out why my nickname is "Daisy Boots?" Well my parents decided my four little white paws were just too cute to be ignored, so most often they just call me "Boots" (unless I'm in big trouble and then I get called by my full name and trust me when you're a puppy that happens quite often).

As my theme song suggests, I'm the new pup on the block. Megyn needed a new playmate since Sydney is getting a bit older and less playful. I am another rescue dog saved by *Border Collies in Need* just like my sister Megyn.

Mommy found me on their website in November 2013 and brought Megyn to meet me to see if we would get along. I was mellow as could be that day. After being a stray for quite some time up in Northern California I was tired of running. That turned out to be my adoption day and in my mind the day I hit the jackpot. I was so exhausted from all my ordeals that my new daddy had to carry me out of the adoption event like a little baby.

Living with two new sisters was a bit challenging. Sydney definitely let me know that she was in charge and that I was pretty low on the food chain. But gradually she has learned to love me and has even handed over some of her old jobs to me so that she has ample time for puppy naps. Megyn and I became best buddies and playmates instantly. We love tugging on ropes and wrestling together.

I'm smart as a whip with a few inexplicable peculiar habits, but everyone just says it's because I'm a border collie. For example, I don't see a reason for toys to be left inside so I make sure all the ropes are always out in the yard. Actually anything on the floor is fair game, so if you leave anything there it will end up in the backyard eventually. I'm not much of a herder but I do like chasing birds and bugs in the yard. The only creature I do try to herd is my sister Sydney, but she doesn't respect my authority and usually just ignores me when I stalk her.

I also moonlight as a piano technician and love to help mommy when she is working on fixing up her piano. One time she left a box full of brand new hammers for me to "install." She didn't seem very happy about the decorative teeth marks that I added to them, but boy were those some yummy chewie sticks!

I love wearing my red bandana every single day and snuggling at night with my daddy. My other favorite thing to do is to relax in my *condo*. Some people call it a crate, but it's far too luxurious to be referred to that way. I love my family to pieces and I know they love the carefree puppy energy that I've brought into their lives as well.

New Kid on the Block

Carefree swing

Jennifer Eklund

Copyright © 2014 Piano Pronto Publishing, Inc.
All Rights Reserved | PianoPronto.com

Walkin' Tall

Jennifer Eklund

Copyright © 2013 Piano Pronto Publishing, Inc.
All Rights Reserved | PianoPronto.com

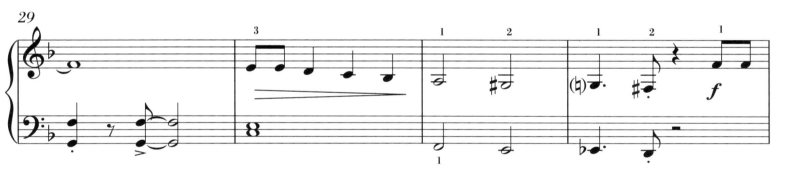

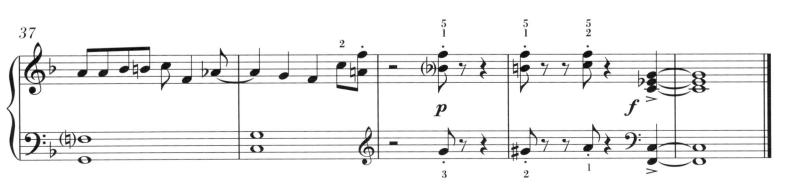

Lullaby

Andante with rubato

Jennifer Eklund

Copyright © 2013 Piano Pronto Publishing, Inc.
All Rights Reserved | PianoPronto.com

PIANO PRONTO®